Cut Here.

A surgeon mom's letter to her little boy

Written by
Katrina B. Mitchell,
MD, IBCLC

Illustrated by
Kate Fallahee

Printed by Ingram Spark in the United States of America

First Printing, 2020

ISBN: 978-0-578-65777-6

To my mom,

Thank you for all you have done in my life.
Most of all, thank you for showing me
how to be a mom myself.
I love you.

Dear B,

You were born and changed my life.
I was pregnant and gave birth to you
during my surgical training.

It was a challenge to realign priorities.
You were always number one,
but I also loved my work.

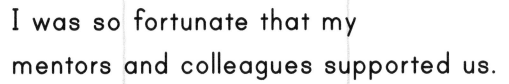
I was so fortunate that my
mentors and colleagues supported us.

You attended your first surgery conference when you were three months old!

I didn't sleep very much during
that last year of training.
But it was all worth it.
I can't imagine life without you.

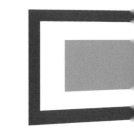

Getting to breastfeed and snuggle with you at night was priceless. I pumped milk for you at all hours.

You were right there by my side when I started my first surgical practice.
You have grown up watching me talk on the phone to patients and wear scrubs to work.

It made me so proud
when you first asked
to go to work with me,
and wanted your
own scrubs.

It made me even prouder that you tell everyone you want to be a doctor like your mom.

In the morning, you call from the playground, "have fun at work today, mommy!"

I am overjoyed you see my work
as a positive part of our lives.

You are part of who I am,
and inspire the work I do.

I am so privileged to be a surgeon.
It's an amazing calling in life.

I want you to choose your own
path and find what you love, too.

But, for now, I smile when you use excellent technique with your lefthanded scissors.

You ask, "can I operate with you today, mommy?"
And I say, "yes, cut here, little surgeon."

I love you, B.

CPSIA information can be obtained
at www.ICGtesting.com
Printed in the USA
LVHW072141080320
649384LV00013B/660